HENRY'S HAT

By Eric & Joanna Johnson
Illustrated by Eric Johnson

SLATE
FALLS
PRESS

Slate Falls Press, LLC
P.O. Box 7062
Loveland, CO 80537
www.slatefallspress.com

Library of Congress Cataloging-in-Publication Data Johnson, Joanna.
Henry's Hat / by Joanna Johnson illustrations by Eric Johnson
ISBN 978-0578172248 ISBN 0578172240
Signature Book Printing, inc.
www.sbpbooks.com
Printed in the U.S.A.

for Grant

One sunny summer morning, Henry Chipmunk was playing downstairs in his cozy burrow home building a sofa fort. Henry was wearing his favorite green hand-knit hat, which he called his "imagination" hat. You could never be quite sure who Henry was pretending to be when he wore his green hat!

"Time to eat!" called Henry's sister from the kitchen upstairs.

Henry's family, along with Aunt Violet, gathered together around their cedar table to a breakfast of acorn pancakes topped with elderberry jam. Henry loved berries more than anything else, and was busily clanking his knife trying to get that last little bit of jam from the jar.

"That is our last jar of jam," said Henry's father. "The elderberries down in the glen are ripe, so we will all be going down with the Robins to harvest berries tomorrow."

The next day they all walked to the glen carrying berry baskets, a wheelbarrow, and their tallest ladder. Henry's father worked picking elderberries from the top of the high ladder while Henry stayed safe down below, emptying the full baskets of berries into the wheelbarrow. Aunt Violet and Mrs. Robin sat spinning and knitting as they chit-chatted together.

Henry noticed a very plump bunch of berries hanging further out on a branch over the creek. He left the wheelbarrow and, grabbing a basket, climbed through the elderberry bush to pick them. He began tugging away at the berries and filling his basket.

"Don't hang from the green branches!" called out one of the Robin boys, but just then, the branch gave way and Henry went tumbling backwards down toward the rushing water below!

Luckily for Henry, he landed on a rhododendron bush and was saved from falling into the rocky creek and being swept away to the waterfall just downstream from the berry patch. Henry's father and Mr. Robin rushed upstream to a fallen tree and crossed the creek, carrying the ladder with them. Mr. Toad helped hold the ladder as Henry's father climbed out over the rough waters to rescue Henry. He clung tightly to the ladder as he returned to safe and sound to solid ground and was very thankful to be with his family once again!

The Chipmunks all worked together to make a big batch of elderberry jam to put up for the coming winter. As summer ended, they filled their underground storehouse with an abundance of food for the coming cold months. Early one fall morning, Henry awoke eager to play and searched high and low for his favorite green hat but he could not find it anywhere.

"When do you last remember wearing your hat?" his father asked him.

"Oh! I remember I had it on when we went berry picking with the Robins. I must have lost it when I fell!" said Henry. "I will go to the glen tomorrow to look for it."

Henry headed for the glen, enjoying the sweet cool autumn air. He searched the rocky glen all along the creek where he fell but he couldn't find his hat.

"I must be like a detective and look for clues," he told himself.

So he headed downstream along the creek bed to the home of the Beavers, who lived just below the waterfall, and asked them if they had seen his hat.

"Hi, Steve, I think I lost my favorite hat this past summer while berry picking upstream, it is my green hat. Have you seen it?"

"Hmmm... come to think of it, not long ago, I saw Ollie Otter out along the far side of the pool trying to catch some minnows with a net. But the net looked odd, and was the same color green as your hat. Does that help?"

"Yes! Oh, boy!" said Henry, filling with hope. "My first clue!"

The next morning Henry headed out to find Ollie Otter. As he walked through the meadow, he passed Old Man Mole, who had just popped out from his earthy tunnel.

"Good day, Mr. Mole, " said Henry politely. "I lost my favorite green hat back in the creek by the glen and I am trying to find it. I think Ollie Otter might know where it is so I am on my way to see him."

"A green hat, you say?" said Mr. Mole. "Well, I saw something that looked like your hat when I was looking for worms out by Slate Falls Mill a while back. I saw two short-tailed shrew twins harvesting sunflower seeds out by the corn field and they were putting the seeds into a fuzzy green basket that looked a lot like your hat."

Henry's eyes widened. "Another clue!" But the mill was even further downstream. Thinking about those sunflower seeds made him hungry, which reminded him to head home for lunch.

Henry woke before sunrise the next day, eager to find his way to the mill to find the shrew twins. As he passed through the dark forest, he heard something overhead, and looked up to see his friend Charlie the Flying Squirrel.

"Henry! You are up early!" he said.

"Hello there, Charlie. I am out trying to find my favorite green hat. I lost it while berry picking this summer," replied Henry.

"I remember that hat!" said Charlie. "You know, last week I was out by Mountain Laurel Spring and I saw Mrs. Raccoon washing her cubs with a strange green washcloth. Maybe it was your hat?"

"Really?" exclaimed Henry. "Thanks, friend!" Henry rushed off, heading in the direction of the Raccoon family den over the hill. "A third clue!" he thought to himself.

Henry made his way along the stream on his was to the home of the Raccoons. As he was walking along, he noticed something overhead in a tall beech tree. It looked like a flycatcher's nest, up in the branches. He saw what looked like some green strands of yarn dangling from the bottom of the nest. As he stood looking up at the nest, a sinking feeling slowly came over him as he realized that he had just found his hat. It had been unraveled and woven into the bird's nest.

Henry returned home with the bad news. His father patted his head and his mother hugged him and made a batch of his favorite cookies. Although the weather was getting colder by the day, the Chipmunks were ready for the coming winter. They all busied themselves with work to do inside the house to prepare for Thanksgiving. They always enjoyed a great feast with their woodland friends and family. Everyone chipped in to help. Father sang loudly while he carried in wood for the stove, Henry's sister was baking fresh rolls, his brother was setting the table and Aunt Violet was working on making a new project with her yarn and knitting needles.

At last it was time to celebrate. What a feast they shared! The Chipmunks served roast acorn apricot loaf with wild onion gravy, crabapple and walnut dumplings, wild strawberry soup, steamed sunflower seeds, fresh pine nuts, wild oat rolls with elderberry jam, blueberry-mint juice and wineberry cordial for the grown-ups. When it was time for dessert, Henry's mother brought out her famous chocolate cake shaped like a yule log. Henry's father proposed a toast and everyone cheered.

"It's snowing!" someone excitedly called out. It was the first snow of the year. After dessert, the children bundled up into their coats, hats, mittens and boots. As Henry was getting ready, Aunt Violet called to him. She presented him with a newly knit green hat, just like Henry's favorite hat that he had lost! Henry was so happy that he gave Aunt Violet a gigantic hug. The Chipmunk family's home was filled with warmth and love.

The children all ran out to play in the snowy woodland. Henry felt very thankful for his family and friends. After picking teams, the children played a fantastic game of football. Henry caught the ball and scored the game-winning touchdown for his team! It was a Thanksgiving that he would always remember.

the end

Henry's Hat

Size

Child small: 2-4 (medium: 6-8, large: 10-12)

Head circumference 19 (20, 21) inches

Shown in size 6-8

Yarn

Brown Sheep Company Lanaloft Worsted, 100% wool, 160 yards per 100 grams.

Scottish Hillside (green) or Blue Fir (blue), 1 skein.

Needles

Size US 8 12-inch circular and/or double-pointed needles

Gauge

18 stitches over 4 inches in reverse stockinette stitch

Notions

Stitch markers, tapestry needle, waste yarn, 2 buttons, ¾ to 1 inch in size

Pattern Notes

The ear and front flaps for the hat are worked first and connected on the first row worked in the round. The hat is then worked from the brim up to the crown. Note that the hat is worked inside out- when you are completed with the knitting, you will turn the hat inside out (actually, right side out) before blocking.

Pattern

Front Flap

CO 18 sts.

Knit 2 rows.

K1, kfb, k to last 3 sts, kfb, k2. 20 sts.

Knit 1 row.

Buttonhole row: k2, BO 2, k to last 4 sts, BO 2, k2.

Next row: k2, CO 2 using the backward loop method, k to BO sts, CO 2 using the backward loop method, k2.

Knit 12 rows straight.

Cut yarn and place live sts on a holder to be joined later.

Ear Flap (make 2)

CO 6 sts.

Knit 2 rows.

Row 1: k1, kfb, k to last 3 sts, kfb, k2

Row 2: knit

Repeat these 2 rows 3 times more. 14 sts.

Knit 8 rows straight.

Cut yarn and place live sts on a holder to be joined later.

Hat Brim

Using short circular needle or double-pointed needles, attach flaps to crown of hat as follows:

Using the backward loop method throughout row, CO 2 to right hand needle, knit 14 sts from ear flap, CO 6 (8, 10), knit 20 sts from front flap, CO 6 (8, 10), knit 14 from remaining ear flap, CO 16 (18, 20). 78 (84, 90) sts.

Place marker and join for working in the round, being careful not to twist sts.

Row 1: knit around

Row 2: purl around

Repeat these two rounds three times more.

Purl 10 rounds.

Row 1: knit around

Row 2: purl around

Repeat these two rounds once more.

Shape Crown

(You should already have a marker in place to mark the beginning of the round, it helps if it is unique from the other markers you are about to place.)

Place markers as follows: * K 11 (12, 13) pm, k2, pm * repeat from * to * six times total.

Begin working in crown pattern as follows: * k to marker, slip marker, p2, slip marker * repeat from * to * six times total.

Repeat this round five times more.

Decrease round: (ssk, knit to last 2 sts before marker, k2tog, p2) repeat six times. 12 sts dec. 66 (72, 78) sts rem.

Work crown pattern round as established twice more.

Begin series of decrease rounds as follows, switching to double-pointed needles as necessary as you go.

Work decrease round. 54 (60, 66) sts.

Work crown pattern round as established twice more.

Work decrease round. 42 (48, 54) sts.

Work crown pattern round as established once.

Work decrease round. 30 (36, 42) sts.

Work crown pattern round as established once more, removing markers as you go.

Size small 2-4 only:

(K3tog, k2) six times. 18 sts rem.

(K2tog, k1) six times. 12 sts rem.

K2tog six times. 6 sts rem.

Size medium 6-8 only:

(Ssk, k2tog, p2) six times. 24 sts rem.

(K2, p2) repeat across round.

(K2tog, p2) six times. 18 sts rem.

(K2tog, k1) six times. 12 sts rem.

K2tog six times. 6 sts rem.

Size large 10-12 only:

(Ssk, k1, k2tog, p2) six times. 30 sts rem.

(K3, p2) repeat across round.

(K2tog, k1, p2) six times. 24 sts rem.

(K2tog, k2) six times. 18 sts rem.

(K2tog, k1) six times. 12 sts rem.

K2tog six times. 6 sts rem.

All sizes: Cut yarn, draw through the stitches.

Finishing: Weave in ends.

Turn hat inside out, and block according to your favorite method.

Fold up front flap and secure with buttons as shown in the photos.

Henry's Letter Sweater

Size

Child 2 (4, 6, 8, 10, 12)

Chest circumference of finished garment is 24 (26, 28, 30, 32, 34) inches

Shown in size 6, boy; size 8, girl

Yarn

Brown Sheep Company Lanaloft Worsted, 100% wool, 160 yards per 100 grams.

Manor Grey 2 (2, 2, 2, 3, 3) skeins, Cottage White 2 (2, 2, 2, 2, 3) skeins, Sleeve Color Scottish Hillside (green) or Blue Fir (blue) 2 (2, 2, 3, 3, 3) skeins, contrast color for duplicate stitch letter, Cliff Rock, 25 yards.

Needles

Size US 7 16-inch and 24-inch circular needles, also, double-pointed needles or 9 or 12-inch circulars for sleeves

Size US 9 16-inch and 24-inch circular needles, also, double-pointed needles or 9 or 12-inch circulars for sleeves

Gauge

18 stitches over 4 inches in stockinette stitch

Notions

Stitch markers, tapestry needle, waste yarn

Pattern Notes

This letterman-inspired pullover is knit in the round from the bottom up. First, you knit the body of the sweater in the stripe pattern as shown, binding off at the neckline. Then, you knit the sleeves one-at-a-time from the cuff up, also binding off at the neckline. Using mattress stitch, you seam the sleeves to the body of the sweater along the raglan-shaped shoulder line, and then work a simple garter rib band around the neckline. Lastly, using the alphabet charts provided, you can duplicate stitch a letter onto the front of the sweater to customize the garment for its intended recipient. Happy Knitting!

Sweater Body

With size US 7 24-inch circular needles and gray, cast on 108 (120, 128, 136, 144, 152) sts.

Place marker and join for working in the round, being careful not to twist sts.

Work in garter ribbing for 8 (10, 10, 12, 12, 14) rounds:

Round 1: k2, p2, repeat

Round 2: knit

Switch to size US 9 needles and white yarn and begin working in st st, knitting every row.

Work 4 rows in white, 4 rows in gray, repeat stripe pattern as established, carefully carrying yarn on inside of sweater as you switch colors.

Repeat in stripe pattern until the sweater measures 10 (11, 12 ½, 14 ½, 16 ½, 18) inches from the cast on at the hem. Shorten or lengthen the sweater body at this point to customize the fit.

Divide for front and back as follows:

Sweater Back

Place last 3 (3, 3, 3, 4, 4) stitches and first 3 (3, 3, 3, 4, 4) stitches of round on waste yarn for underarm, to be grafted later.

Place next 48 (54, 58, 62, 64, 68) stitches on a holder for the front.

Place next 6, (6, 6, 6, 8, 8) stitches on waste yarn for underarm, to be grafted later.

Break yarn and begin working on sweater back, beginning with rs facing and working back and forth rather than in the round.

Row 1 (RS): K2, ssk, k to last 4 sts, k2tog, k2. 2 sts dec. 46 (52, 56, 60, 62, 66) sts rem.

Row 2 (WS): purl

Repeat these two rows, keeping in established color stripe pattern, 12 (14, 15, 17, 17, 19) times more. 22 (24, 26, 26, 28, 28) sts remain.

Bind off all stitches.

Sweater Front

Begin working on sweater front, beginning with rs facing and working back and forth rather than in the round.

Row 1 (RS): K2, ssk, k to last 4 sts, k2tog, k2. 2 sts dec. 46 (52, 56, 60, 62, 66) sts rem.

Row 2 (WS): purl

Repeat these two rows, keeping in established color stripe pattern, 9 (11, 12, 14, 15, 16) times more. 28 (30, 32, 32, 32, 34) sts remain.

Shape neck: K2, ssk, k2, BO 16 (18, 20, 20, 22, 22) sts, k2, k2tog, k2.

Turn, p3, p2togtbl, leaving other sts for left side on needle to be worked later.

Turn and BO 4 sts.

With ws facing, work left front, p2tog, p3.

Turn and BO 4 sts.

Sleeves (make 2)

Using size 7 shortest circular or double-pointed needles, cast on 32 (36, 36, 40, 40, 44) sts for sleeve cuff.

Place marker and join for working in the round, being careful not to twist sts.

Begin working in garter rib:

Round 1: K2, p2, repeat across row.

Round 2: Knit.

Repeat these two rows for a total of 12 (12, 14, 16, 16, 16) rounds.

Change to size 9 shortest circular or double-pointed needles and begin increasing for sleeve.

Increase row: k1, m1, knit to last stitch, m1, k1. 2 sts inc. 34 (38, 38, 42, 42, 46) sts.

Knit 7 rows even without shaping.

Repeat these 8 rows 5 (6, 7, 8, 9, 9) times more, 44 (50, 52, 58, 60, 64) sts rem.

Work until sleeve measures 11 (12, 13, 14 ½, 15 ½, 16 ½) inches. Shorten or lengthen the sleeves at this point to customize the fit.

Place last 3 (3, 3, 3, 4, 4) stitches and first 3 (3, 3, 3, 4, 4) stitches of round on waste yarn for underarm, to be grafted later. Break yarn. 38 (44, 46, 52, 52, 56) sts.

Begin working on sleeve with rs facing and working back and forth rather than in the round.

Decrease as for the sweater body as follows:

Row 1 (RS): K2, ssk, k to last 4 sts, k2tog, k2. 2 sts dec. 36 (42, 44, 50, 50, 54) sts rem.

Row 2 (WS): purl

Repeat these two rows 12 (14, 15, 17, 17, 19) times more. 12 (14, 14, 16, 16, 16) sts rem.

Bind off all sts.

Neckband

Graft the underarm seams using stitches from holders, with wrong sides together, using kitchener stitch to join sleeves to sweater body.

Using mattress stitch, sew sleeves to sweater body, carefully matching raglan sleeve seams.

With medium or shortest length size 7 needles, pick up 68 (76, 80, 84, 88, 88) sts around the neckline.

Place marker and join for working in the round.

Round 1: knit

Round 2: k2, p2, repeat across round.

Repeat these two rounds 4 (4, 4, 6, 6, 6) times more.

Bind off all sts loosely.

Finishing

Weave in all ends, block to desired measurements.

Using alphabet charts provided, duplicate stitch the letter of your choosing onto the front of the sweater, weave in ends, and block again to even out the duplicate stitching.

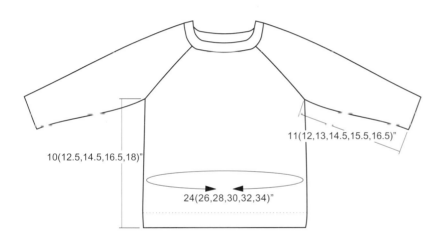

11(12,13,14.5,15.5,16.5)"

10(12.5,14.5,16.5,18)"

24(26,28,30,32,34)"

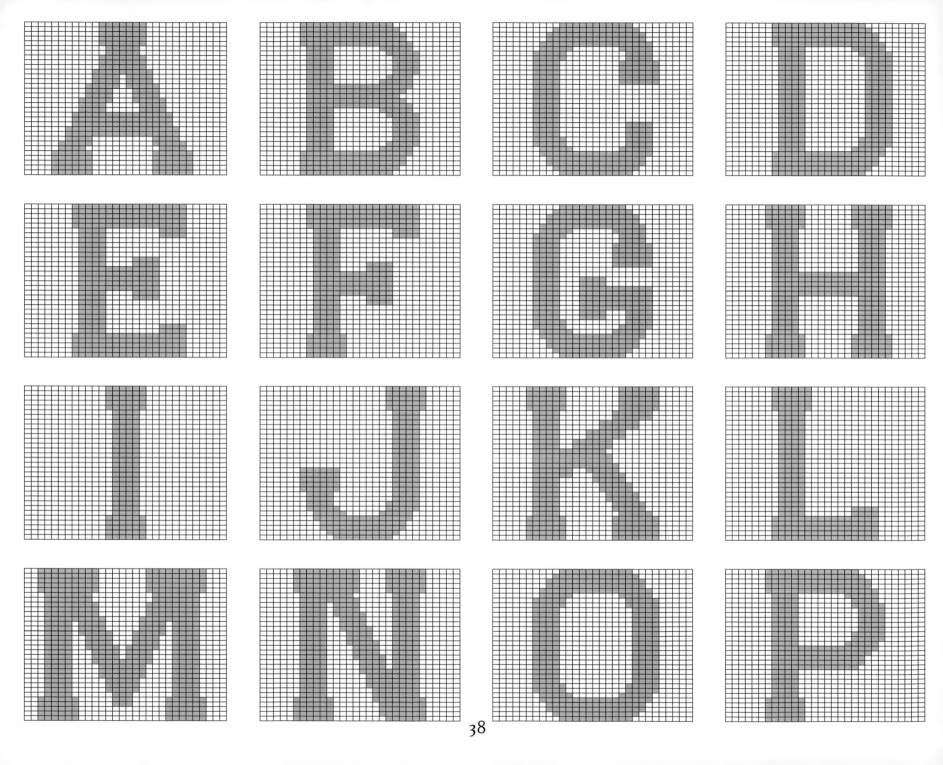

Henry Chipmunk

Size

17 inches tall

Yarn

Brown Sheep Company Lanaloft Worsted, 100% wool, 160 yards per 100 grams

Cliff Rock, 2 skeins

Buckwheat, 20 yards

English Saddle, 20 yards

Scottish Hillside, 60 yards

Blue Fir, 60 yards

Cottage White, 60 yards

Manor Grey, 60 yards

Needles

Size US 5 double-pointed needles

Size US 5 straight or circular needles

Size US 7 double-pointed needles

Size US 9 12-inch circular and/or double-pointed needles

Long (32 inches or longer) circular needle size US 7

Gauge

19 stitches over 4 inches in stockinette stitch on size US 7 needles

16 stitches over 4 inches in stockinette stitch on size US 9 needles

Notions

Stitch markers, tapestry needle, waste yarn, toy stuffing of your choice, one 2" x 4" piece of wool felt in dark brown and one in light tan for the face, ½ yard of ¼ inch elastic

Pattern Notes

Henry Chipmunk is a nearly seamless knit toy worked from the top down in the round. The head is worked separately and stitched on at the end. His adorable facial features are created using simple shapes of wool felt. His sweater is a perfect match to Henry's Sweater, and, if you like, you can add a simple monogram-style letter to match!

Pattern

Chipmunk Toy

Head

Using Cliff Rock and size US 5 double pointed needles, cast on 6 sts. Divide evenly onto three needles. Place marker and join for working in the round, being careful not to twist stitches.

Knit 1 rnd.

Next rnd: * m1, k1 * repeat 6 times. 12 sts.

Next rnd: * m1, k2 * repeat 6 times. 18 sts.

Knit 1 rnd.

Next rnd: * m1, k3 * repeat 6 times. 24 sts.

Knit 1 rnd.

Next rnd: * m1, k4 * repeat 6 times. 30 sts.

Knit 1 rnd.

Next rnd: * m1, k5 * repeat 6 times. 36 sts.

Knit 1 rnd.

Next rnd: * m1, k6 * repeat 6 times. 42 sts.

Knit 1 rnd.

Next rnd: * m1, k7 * repeat 6 times. 48 sts.

Knit 1 rnd.

Next rnd: * m1, k8 * repeat 6 times. 54 sts.

18 sts per needle.

Knit 11 rnds.

Adjust needles to shape face: using four needles place stitches as follows:

Needle 1: 12 sts

Needle 2: 15 sts

Needle 3: 12 sts

Needle 4: 15 sts

Decrease row: (K1, ssk, knit to last 3 sts on needle, k2tog, k1) repeat four times across round. 8 sts dec. 46 sts rem.

Knit two rounds.

Repeat decrease round. 38 sts rem.

Knit 2 rounds.

Repeat decrease round. 30 sts rem.

Knit 2 rounds.

Repeat decrease round. 22 sts.

Knit 1 round.

Decrease as follows: ssk, k2tog, needle 1; k1, ssk, k1, k2tog, k1, needle 2; ssk, k2tog, needle 3; k1, ssk, k1, k2tog, k1, needle 4. 14 sts rem.

Cut yarn leaving a 24-inch tail. Slip live sts onto yarn tail. Block head using steam heat. Weave in cast-on tail, taking note that the cast on stitches are located at the back of the head. Following the face applique templates provided, cut wool felt for the face details as shown. Starting with the larger brown "mask", stack on the light tan, then the thinner brown stripe, finally placing the eye on top. Neatly stitch pieces to one another first, then place on each side of the face and stitch in place, following the shaping of the knit decreases as shown in the photos. Stuff the head, and then close the opening by carefully drawing the stitches together. Using the English Saddle yarn stitch a small "V" for the mouth. See pictures of Henry to help decide size and placement of the "V."

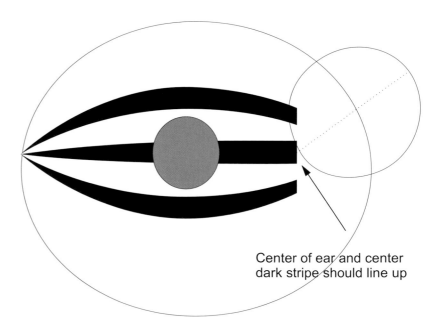

Center of ear and center dark stripe should line up

Body

Using a long tail cast on (and leaving an extra 18 inches of yarn), color Cliff Rock and size US 5 double pointed needles, cast on 6 sts.

Place marker and join for working in the round, being careful not to twist stitches.

Knit 1 round.

Next round: * kfb, * 6 times, 12 sts.

Next round: * kfb, k1 * 6 times, 18 sts.

Next round: * kfb, k2 * 6 times, 24 sts.

Next round: * kfb, k3 * 6 times, 30 sts.

Next round: * kfb, k4 * 6 times, 36 sts.

Next round: * kfb, k5 * 6 times, 42 sts.

Next round: * kfb, k6 * 6 times, 48 sts.

Next round: * kfb, k7 * 6 times, 54 sts.

Next round: * kfb, k8 * 6 times, 60 sts.

Next round: * kfb, k9 * 6 times, 66 sts.

Knit 4 rounds.

Create arm openings:

Next round: knit 22 (needle 1); knit 11 and slip to a piece of waste yarn, knit 11 (needle 2); knit 11, (needle 3), knit 11 and slip to a piece of waste yarn.

Next round: Knit 22 (needle 1); cast on 11 and slip to an empty needle, use this needle to knit 11 from needle 2 (needle 2); knit 11, cast on 11 (needle 3). 66 sts.

Knit 24 rounds, leaving arm opening sts on waste yarn to be picked up later on.

Shape bottom and leg openings:

Knit 11, m1, k1, m1, knit to end of round. 68 sts.

Next round: knit 10, slip to a piece of waste yarn, knit 4, knit 10 and slip to a piece of waste yarn, * k2tog * 10 times, knit 4, * k2tog * 10 times.

Next round: cast on 10 stitches to an empty needle, knit 4, cast on 10 (needle 1); knit 12 (needle 2); knit 12 (needle 3). 48 sts.

Knit 2 rounds even.

Slip sts from needle 3 to needle 2. Place needle 1 next to needle 2 and graft sts using Kitchener stitch. Weave in ends.

Ears (make 2)

With Cliff Rock and size US 5 double pointed needles, cast on 16 sts. Place marker and join for working in the round, being careful not to twist sts. Place sts on needles as follows:

Needle 1: 8 sts

Needle 2: 4 sts

Needle 3: 4 sts

Knit 8 rounds.

Decrease: (ssk, k4, k2tog) twice. 12 sts rem.

Decrease: (ssk, k2, k2tog) twice. 8 sts rem.

Cut yarn, leaving a 12 inch tail. Draw yarn tail through live sts.

Stitch ears onto the head, weave in ends.

Create back stripes and tail:

Using US size 5 straight or circular needles and Cliff Rock, cast on 20 sts.

Beginning with a knit row work stockinette stitch back and forth for 4 rows.

Next row: work across 20 sts, do not turn work, and using backward loop cast on, cast on 22 sts.

With English Saddle, purl 1 row.

With Buckwheat knit 1 row.

With Buckwheat purl 1 row.

With Cliff Rock knit 1 row.

With English Saddle purl 1 row.

With Cliff Rock knit 1 row.

With Buckwheat purl 1 row.

With Buckwheat knit 1 row.

With English Saddle purl 1 row.

Continue working in Cliff Rock:

Knit 1 row.

Bind off 22 sts kw, purl to end of row.

Work in stockinette stitch for 5 rows.

Bind off all sts kw. Block stripes and tail.

Using photos as a guide, place the narrow edge of the stripes at the top of the toy body, with the tail at the base of the body. Carefully stitch the stripes onto the back of the toy, and, when you get to the tail section, fold the tail under itself so the cast on edge and bound off edge meet up, stitching along this edge to close up the tail.

Arms

Pick up 11 sts for arm from waste yarn. Pick up another 13 sts around arm opening. 24 sts. Join for working in the round and knit 30 rounds.

Decrease: * k2, k2tog * 6 times. 18 sts rem.

Knit 1 round.

Decrease: * k1, k2tog * 6 times. 12 sts rem.

Cut yarn leaving a 12-inch tail. Draw yarn tail through live stitches and fasten off. Weave in ends.

Repeat for the second arm.

Block body and arms. Using the toy stuffing of your choice, fill arms and toy torso through the leg openings.

Legs

Pick up 10 sts for leg from waste yarn. Pick up 14 sts around leg opening. 24 sts. Knit every round for 40 rounds.

Decrease: * k2, k2tog * 6 times. 18 sts rem.

Knit 1 round.

Decrease: * k1, k2tog * 6 times. 12 sts rem.

Cut yarn leaving a 12-inch tail and thread live stitches onto yarn tail. Block legs. Stuff leg and body to completion. Draw yarn tail through live stitches and fasten off. Repeat for second leg.

Sew head to chipmunk body.

Toy Sweater

With size US 7 double pointed needles and Manor Grey, cast on 68 sts. Place marker and join for working in the round, being careful not to twist stitches.

Work in garter rib in the round:

Round 1: k2, p2 repeat across round

Round 2: knit around

Repeat these two rounds once more.

Switch to size US 9 needles and begin working stockinette stitch in the round, creating the stripe pattern as follows:

Knit 2 rounds in Cottage White

Knit 2 rounds in Manor Grey

Work in this pattern as established for 18 rounds total. Break yarn.

Place last 2 sts of round and first 2 sts of round on a piece of waste yarn to be worked later.

Place next 30 sts on waste yarn for the sweater back. Place next 4 sts on a piece of waste yarn for the underarm to be worked later.

Begin working back and forth on sweater front starting with the right side facing you.

Keeping stripe pattern as established, shape raglan shoulder.

Row 1: K1, ssk, knit to last 3 sts, k2tog, k1.

Row 2: Purl

Repeat these 2 rows 5 times more.

18 sts remain. BO all sts.

Repeat raglan shaping for the back.

Sleeves (make 2)

Using size US 7 double pointed needles and Scottish Hillside, cast on 24 sts. Place marker and join for working in the round, being careful not to twist stitches.

Work in garter rib in the round:

Row 1: k2, p2 repeat

Row 2: knit around

Repeat these two rounds once more.

Switch to size US 9 needles and knit every round for 14 rounds.

Slip last 2 sts and first 2 sts of round onto a piece of waste yarn to be worked later.

Begin working back and forth, shape raglan seam.

Row 1: K1, ssk, knit to last 3 sts, k2tog, k1.

Row 2: Purl

Repeat these 2 rows 5 times more. 8 sts rem.

Bind off all sts.

Graft sleeves to the body using 3-needle bind off at underarm. Sew sleeves to the body carefully using mattress stitch.

Using size US 7 needles, pick up and knit 44 stitches around neck opening.

Work in garter rib in the round:

Round 1: k2, p2 repeat

Round 2: knit around

Work row 1 once more.

Bind off all stitches.

Weave in ends and block.

Toy Pants

Legs

Using Blue Fir and size US 7 double pointed needles, CO 32 sts. Join for working in the round, being careful not to twist stitches.

Work in garter rib:

Row 1: k2, p2 repeat

Row 2: knit

Repeat these two rows once more.

Switch to stockinette stitch (knit every round) and knit 24 rounds straight.

Cut yarn leaving a 12-inch tail and thread the tail onto the live stitches for joining later.

Make a second pant leg as for the first, do not cut yarn for second leg.

Join legs:

The simplest way to join the legs is to use the magic loop method. Using the long circular needle, knit 32 sts from the first pant leg, then knit 32 sts from the second pant leg, place marker for the beginning of the round.

Knit one round. 64 sts.

Create opening for tail: knit 60 sts, BO 4 sts, remove marker, BO 4 sts, Knit around to bound off sts, using backward loop method, cast on 4 sts, place marker, cast on another 4 sts. Knit to marker. 64 sts.

Knit 10 rounds even.

Switch to size 5 double pointed needles and work in k2, p2 ribbing for 8 rounds.

Bind off all sts. Weave in ends, stitching closed the opening at the leg join.

Weave elastic through ribbing on inside of pants waistband, adjust to fit the toy, stitch to fasten.

abbreviations

BO	bind off
CO	cast on
dec	decreased
inc	increased
k	knit
k2tog	knit 2 together
k3tog	knit 3 together
kfb	knit into front and back of next stitch
kw	knitwise
m1	make one by knitting into the back of the loop just below the next stitch
p	purl
p2tog	purl 2 together
p2togtbl	purl 2 together through the back loop
pm	place marker
rem	remain
rnd	round
rs	right side
sl	slip
ssk	slip slip knit
sts	stitches
st st	stockinette stitch
ws	wrong side

Joanna Johnson has a B.A. in Literature from Drew University and is the author of Phoebe's Sweater, Freddie's Blanket, Phoebe's Birthday and Green Gables Knits. She lives in Loveland, Colorado, with her husband, Eric, and their three children, who are a constant source of inspiration for her stories. Please visit:
www.ravelry.com/designers/joanna-johnson
to learn more about Joanna's knitting designs and patterns.

Eric Johnson has been working in commerical design for two decades as a signwriter, muralist and graphic designer. He has enjoyed returning to his childhood love of drawing by setting pencil to paper to illustrate this book. He lives with his wife, Joanna, and their three children in Loveland, Colorado. Eric is the Craftsy instructor for Picture Book Illustration: Animal Characters. Please visit:
www.craftsy.com/ext/EricJohnson_4831_H
to learn more about his Craftsy class.

Deepest thanks to: Our family, friends and readers for their encouragement and love. Peggy Jo Wells and the entire staff at Brown Sheep Company, for offering yarn support for the projects in this book. Christa Tippmann, our photographer, for her fine images. Hadley Austin, our technical editor, for her invaluable feedback. Megan Helzer, our copy editor, for her kind attention to detail. Mr. and Mrs. Green of Loveland, Colorado, for allowing us to photograph this book on their property. Our models: Grant Johnson and Piper Holt, for being so cute and fun during the entire photo shoot. Our test knitters: Linsay Cocker, for her enthusiasm; Tamara Cramer, for her support; Megan Helzer, for her faithfulness; Mari Liestman, for her friendship; and Emily Straw, for her continual encouragement. We are thankful for our three children who enrich our lives every day, and to God our Creator for His Light and Love.

Phoebe Mouse
from Phoebe's Sweater

Freddie Platypus
from Freddie's Blanket

Phoebe Mermouse
from Phoebe's Birthday

Henry Chipmunk
from Henry's Hat